How to use this book

Follow the advice, in italics, given for you on each page.
Support the children as they read the text that is shaded in cream.
***Praise** the children at every step!*

Detailed guidance is provided in the Read Write Inc. Phonics Handbook.

8 reading activities

Children:

- *Practise reading the speed sounds.*
- *Read the green, red and challenge words for the story.*
- *Listen as you read the introduction.*
- *Discuss the vocabulary check with you.*
- *Read the story.*
- *Re-read the story and discuss the 'questions to talk about'.*
- *Re-read the story with fluency and expression.*
- *Practise reading the speed words.*

Speed sounds

Consonants *Say the pure sounds (do not add 'uh').*

f ff	l ll	m	n	r	s ss	v ve	z zz s	**sh**	**th**	**ng** nk

b bb	c k **ck**	d	g gg	h	j	p **pp**	qu	t	w wh	x	y	ch tch

Vowels *Say the vowel sound and then the word, eg 'a', 'at'.*

at	hen	in	on	up	day	see	high	blow	zoo

Each box contains one sound but sometimes more than one grapheme. Focus graphemes are ***circled****.*

Green words

Read in Fred Talk (pure sounds).

mat got but lid went back dog

this help shot zing shelf

Read in syllables.

popp' ing → popping

Red words

some into the of said going he out* popcorn*

** Red word for this book only*

Vocabulary check

Discuss the meaning (as used in the story) after the children have read the word.

	definition:
popcorn	*grains of corn which explode and puff up when cooked*

Punctuation to note in this story:

Dan Jan	*Capital letters for names*
It Helps This	*Capital letters that start sentences*
.	*Full stop at the end of each sentence*
!	*Exclamation mark used to show surprise*

Popcorn

Introduction

Have you ever tried making popcorn? As Jan finds out in this story, it makes lots of noise as it cooks! As the popcorn gets hot it pops right out of the pan and lands in all sorts of strange places!

Luckily Jan's brother Dan knows what to do to stop it popping. Let's find out what happens.

Story written by Cynthia Rider
Illustrated by Tim Archbold

Jan put some popcorn
into a pan.

But as it got hot, the popcorn shot out of the pan with a zing, whizz, pop!

It went pop on the shelf and whizz on the mat.

It went ping on the dog and
zing on the cat.

"Help!" said Jan,
"It will not stop!

It will not stop going
zing, whizz, pop!"